MY MANY COLORED DAYS

By Dr. Seuss

PAINTINGS BY
STEVE JOHNSON and LOU FANCHER

SCHOLASTIC INC.
New York Toronto London Auckland Sydney

Some days are yellow.

Some are blue.

On different days
I'm different too.

You'd be
surprised
how many ways

I change
on Different
Colored
Days.

On Bright Red Days
how **good** it feels
to be a horse
and **kick** my heels!

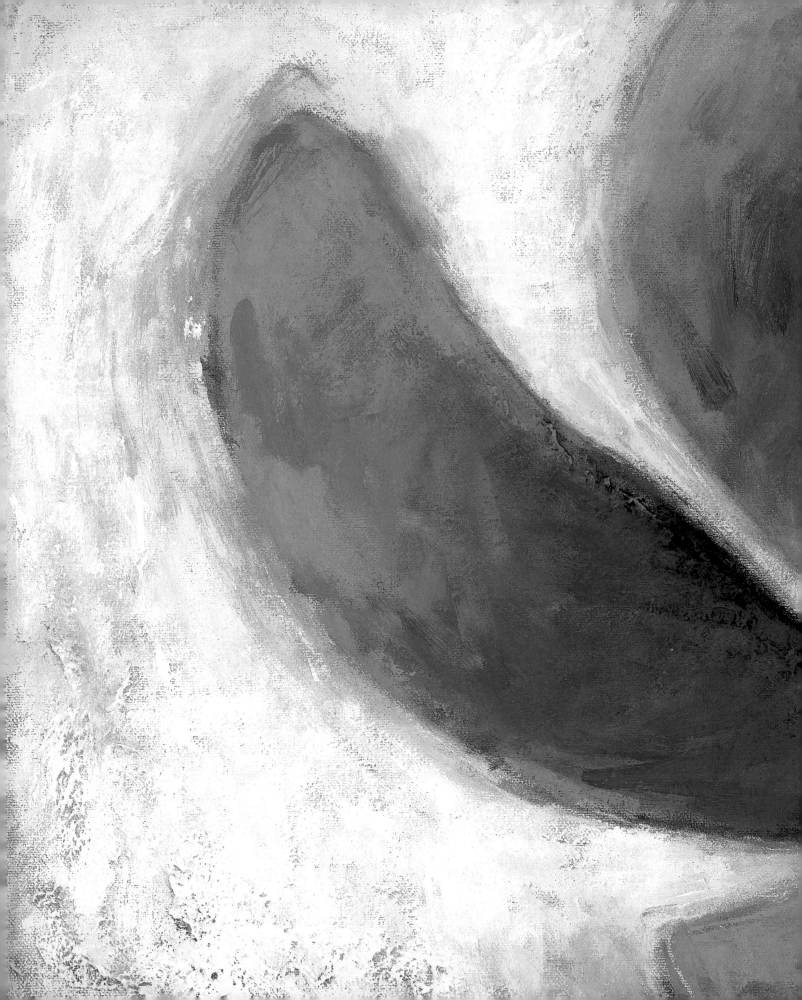

On other days I'm other things.

On Bright Blue Days

I flap my wings.

Some days, of course,
feel sort of Brown.

Then I feel slow
and low,

low

down.

Then comes a Yellow Day.

And,

W H E E E E E

I am a busy, buzzy bee.

Gray Day . . . Everything is gray.

I watch. But nothing moves today.

Then
all of a sudden

I'm a

circus seal!

On my Orange Days
that's how I feel.

Green Days. Deep deep in the sea.

Cool and quiet **fish. That's me.**

On Purple Days

I'm sad.

I *groan.*

I drag my tail.

I walk alone.

But when my days are Happy

Pink

jump

it's great to j and just not think.

Then come my **Black Days.**
MAD. And

loud.

I howl.
I growl at every cloud.

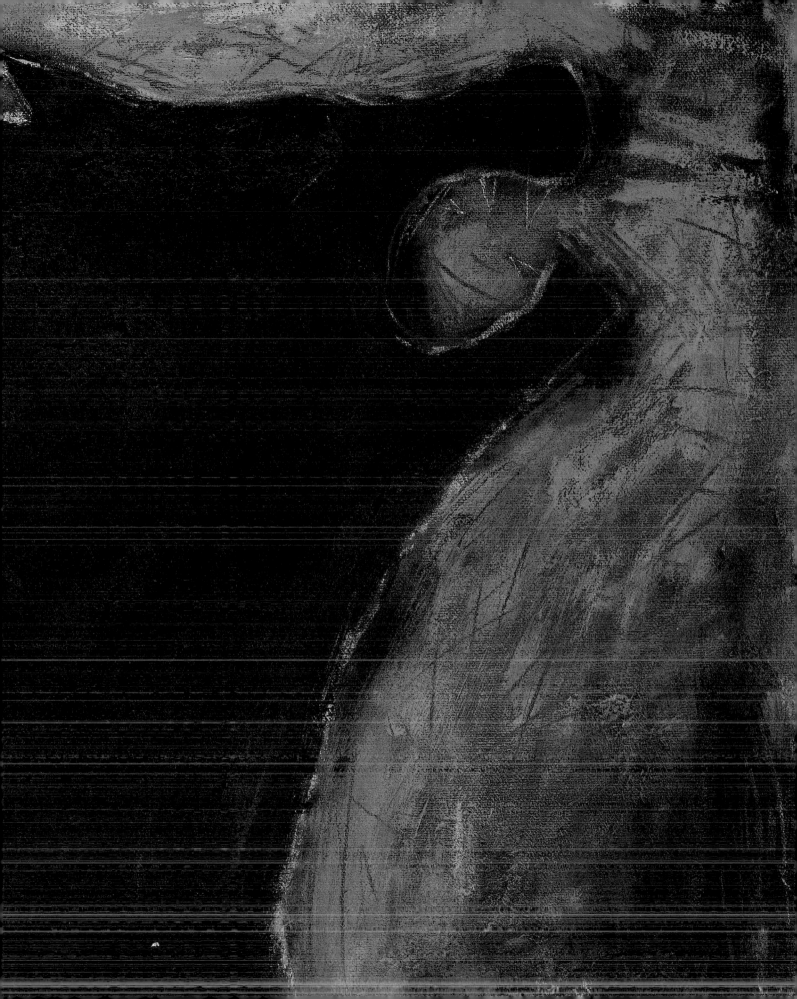

Then comes a Mixed-Up Day.

And **WHAM!**

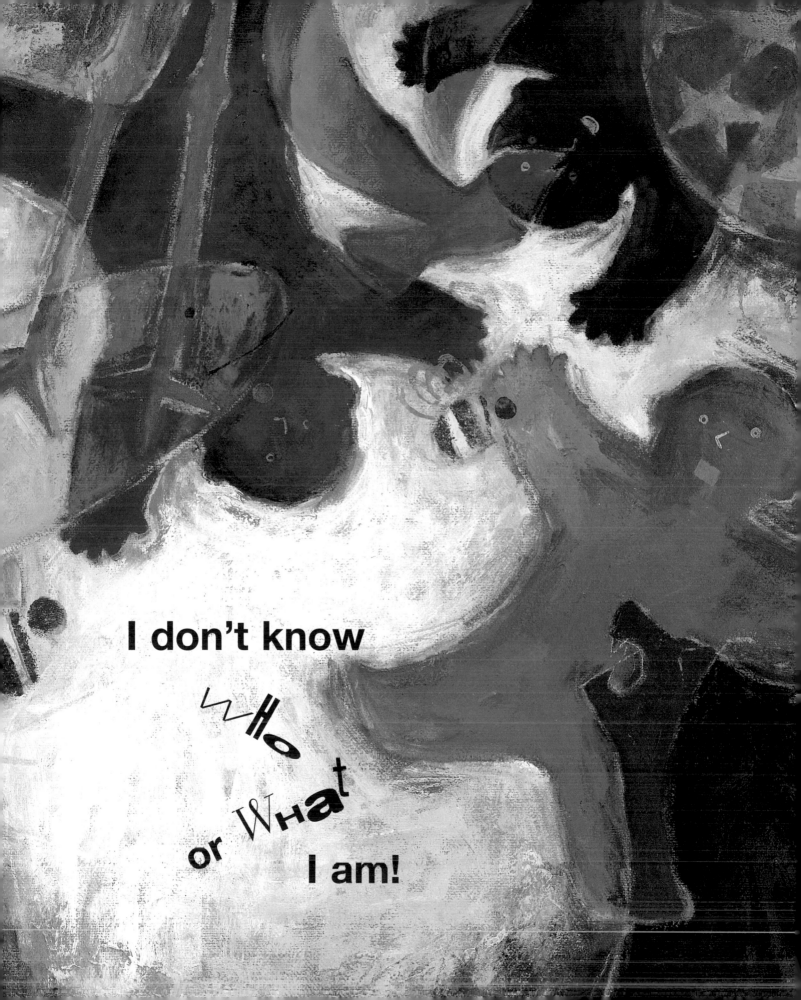

But it all
turns out all right,
you see.

And I go back
to being . . .

me.

To Ted, who colored my days...and my life.

—Audrey Geisel

For Denise and Frances.

—Steve Johnson and Lou Fancher

ISBN 0-590-37046-4

12 11 10 9 8 7 6 5 4   7 8 9/9 0 1 2/0

Printed in the U.S.A.   37

First Scholastic printing, March 1997